EVIE'S DIARY

EVIE'S DIARY

HEATHER COOK

PHOTOGRAPHS BY ROGER COOK

Matador
9 Priory Business Park,
Wistow Road, Kibworth Beauchamp,
Leicestershire. LE8 0RX
Tel: (+44) 116 279 2299
Fax: (+44) 116 279 2277
Email: books@troubador.co.uk
Web: www.troubador.co.uk/matador

ISBN 978 1780883 274

British Library Cataloguing in Publication Data.
A catalogue record for this book is available from the British Library.

Typeset in 12pt Book Antiqua by Troubador Publishing Ltd, Leicester, UK

Matador is an imprint of Troubador Publishing Ltd

Printed and bound in the UK by TJ International, Padstow, Cornwall

This book is dedicated to Poor Roger, my long-suffering husband, who only married me because he loved my cats.

INTRODUCTION

There are kind cats, sulky cats, friendly cats, hero cats – and cats like Evie who despise the human race and consider themselves infinitely superior to the slow, lumpy creatures who care for them and love them beyond all that is reasonable.

Evie is small, smart and black. Her coat is short and lustrous and she is absolutely stunning. Her face is beautiful in a sullen kind of way and her habitual expression is a humbling combination of boredom and contempt.

I first met Evie when she was about three months old. She was one of a litter of three kittens born to a stray domestic mother who graciously allowed people to feed her but failed to reveal the whereabouts of her babies until they had already mastered an impressive vocabulary of swear words and were about as easy to handle as a particularly tricky Tasmanian Devil.

In no time at all, these large and unruly kittens had discovered how to get into the kitchen of the nearest house and would rampage around, helping themselves to anything they fancied. Their mother would watch with an indulgent – or possibly bored – expression while her appalling offspring bullied the well-intentioned couple who occasionally popped in to make a cup of tea.

After a while the couple began to worry, as well they might. Having three kittens trashing their kitchen was bad enough, but they knew enough about cats to realise things wouldn't stop there. A few nightmares about a multi-coloured furry army barring their way to the fridge encouraged them to seek help.

I was heavily involved with cat rescue as the Homing Officer for the Woking Branch of Cats Protection, and I rose to the challenge with what can only be described as misplaced confidence. As soon as I had the call to confirm that all three kittens had been shut in the kitchen, I grabbed my trusty gauntlets and shot off to round them up.

The first two kittens gave up at a fairly early stage, after several circuits of the kitchen and some mild expletives on both sides. With them safely banged up in an escape-proof carrier, I turned my attention to the third kitten, a sweet-looking little black girl. Twenty minutes later, the room resembled a war zone. There was blood everywhere (mine) and the floor was covered with cooking utensils and a range of food-related debris. The lady of the house was still in her wheelchair, but only just, following several bruising encounters with my own substantial frame as I ricocheted from wall to wall.

This kitten had no sense of fair play and fought like a tiger till I finally shoved the ungrateful creature into the waiting cat carrier. Her teeth sliced through my reinforced gauntlets – guaranteed to withstand alligators and rabid dogs, but apparently not small kittens. There are no prizes for realising that this sweet, defenceless creature was none other than little Evie and no prizes either for suggesting that the sensible thing would have been to leave her to make her own arrangements.

I am proud to say that this is not the way with Cats Protection volunteers. We are driven by a passion to help all cats and kittens, even sulky, bad-mannered ones like Evie, and we cling to the belief that time and kindness will move mountains. Of course, it's not usually the mountains that cause the problems.

The other two kittens progressed rapidly to the stage where they only savaged me when there was nothing on the telly, and soon convinced two vulnerable people in search of kittens that they should give them a home. The lovely couple who had endured so much decided to keep the mother cat and we arranged for her to be spayed and inoculated. Eventually, Evie also moved on but was returned within a short time as she refused to sit on laps. I refrained from saying it was more likely that the Loch Ness Monster would pop round and snuggle up on the sofa, and an unrepentant Evie went off to be fostered, on behalf of Cats Protection, by our very own cat whisperer, Karen.

By this time, Evie had been spayed and had ripped the vet to pieces when he attempted to remove her stitches. Karen knew better than to push her luck with the new girl, relying on play to establish a relationship. A year before Evie went to be fostered by Karen, my husband Roger and I had adopted two kittens – Benjamin Wobble, a sweet ginger boy with mobility problems, and his brother Billy, an extremely handsome tabby.

Both kittens had suffered severe illnesses as tiny kittens and were left with a legacy of problems, including a tendency to have violent fits. Although Benjamin's wobbly walk was the most obvious sign of past traumas, it was poor Billy who suffered the longer lasting fits and one such episode resulted in his sudden and untimely death.

This tragedy left our beloved brain-damaged ginger boy without a playmate as the other residents of the "Special Needs Unit" were all on the dribbly side of ancient, so we decided to adopt little Evie as she needed to settle into a permanent home to make way for the influx of kittens that would soon be coming into the care of Cats Protection.

Her diary begins with her arrival at Tresta Towers. I would like to say that these pages are bursting with gratitude and love for the Earth Mother, Poor Roger and her feline companions, but nobody who knows anything about cats would believe that.

CHAPTER ONE

Treacherous Humans!

Whatever's happening? I've been dragged out of my comfy, smelly old igloo and bundled into a cat carrier by my Cats Protection fosterer, who I thought was my friend. Well, has she got it coming! She's cooing at me now through the wire. Forget it! If she thinks I'm going to purr and do headrubs against her treacherous skinny little fingers, she's piddling in the wrong dirt tray.

We're juddering down the road and I can feel a mega chuck-up coming on. We shudder to a halt while I heave and dribble all over the passenger seat. I am living proof that a black cat can look and feel pale, and the human looks pretty fragile too after all that mopping up and the ever-present threat of tail-end action.

We arrive at a boring looking bungalow and an even more boring looking woman lurches out to meet us. I'm decanted into a large cage in what appears to be a home for the elderly, the bewildered and the criminally insane, and immediately plunge into the recesses of a revoltingly new and unblemished igloo.

The boring woman peers at me. 'Bless her,' she twitters, 'poor little Evie's frightened!'

Believe me, only an idiot wouldn't be frightened. A succession of feline misfits passes by, including one that looks like a mobile mop and a wobbly ginger creature

1

that falls over when anybody so much as looks at him. Just as I think I've seen it all, another exhibit enters the room. This one pre-dates the dinosaurs and is as blind as a bat.

Next Morning

I wake up to find my cage has shifted across the room and my igloo is squashed against the side with me in it. The wobbly lump seems fascinated by me and is bracing himself against the wall unit so that he can push my cage across the floor. I spit in his silly ginger face, but this only serves to make me more interesting and he shoves a porky paw through the wire to poke me in the chops.

A major project involving lots of planks of wood and an army of men commences after breakfast and the Earth Mother – as I gather the boring woman is known – is in her element until an unfortunate incident with a tea tray brings about an abrupt change of mood. Miss Isabelle – a perky little black and white number who could gossip for England – tells me that one of the men had abandoned the teacups and tray on the patio, resulting in the poor old EM doing an unplanned toboggan run across the garden. The language was unbelievable but I do remember the vet using similar words when the Treacherous One took me to have my spay stitches out recently.

The wretched man said I was obviously a wild animal and he was blacklisting me. *Him* blacklisting *me*? I'd already crossed him off my Christmas card list long before he wiped his great sausage-like fingers over my delicate little body!

A dreadful night with that Benjamin Wobble creature fumbling with my ping pong ball. Tried kicking cat litter in his face but as usual this seemed to excite him all the more.

The EM has a friend come round for lunch and the poor deluded visitor makes the mistake of asking about The Project. An hour later, the EM is still dripping on, ignoring the fact that the visitor, Miss Isabelle and myself have all but lapsed into a coma.

I shall record the salient facts for posterity as nobody else is likely to be the slightest bit interested.

Apparently, during the Great Freeze in the early days of the New Year, the fat pointy-nosed badgers dug under the back fence and lured Master Benjamin into the woods. Well, they may not actually have lured him, but the silly dollop disappeared and was missing for three whole days and nights. I would like to record that during this stressful time the EM and Poor Roger – a kindly soul who doesn't deserve to be stuck with this middle-aged diva – comforted and supported each other, but this is not how Miss Isabelle tells it.

Anyway, on the Sunday afternoon, by which time they had all but killed each other, they ventured into the woods to search yet again for the silly lump and found him – none the worse for his experiences, which is more than could be said for the EM and Poor Roger, who cried when he was missing and then cried even more when they found him.

So The Project is an attempt to outwit the badgers and keep little Benjamin safe. It is also designed to restrain Blind Sammy who at 17 years of age, is obsessed with escape plans and is always squirrelling away things which he will make into a dummy if he can ever stay awake long enough.

Where's the RSPCA Inspector?

Something's going on. The EM is being all sickly sweet and saying how cute I look in my igloo, which now has a flat top due to me leaping on it in the night.

I'm so cross with myself! She's tricked me into coming closer to her by placing irresistible kitty biscuits just out of reach. Once I'm near enough, she grabs me by the scruff of the neck and manhandles me into a cat carrier. Bitch woman from hell! She will pay for this. They will all pay – especially that butter-wouldn't-melt-in-my-little-mouth Isabelle. I shall never believe she wasn't in on this.

So here we are at the vet's and two grown women are trying to wrestle me onto the scales. The EM expresses surprise that I weigh 20.5 kilos, then realises her handbag is resting on the corner.

The next bit of excitement is having a needle shoved in my neck, which will apparently protect me from all sorts of evil things but possibly not from Master Benjamin's unwelcome attentions. As we prepare to leave, the EM simpers and says that the next time the vet sees me, I might be wearing an engagement ring. The poor woman looks at the EM in the same way she might have regarded a kangaroo that unexpectedly extracts a mobile phone from its pouch and uses it to register a vote for a *Strictly Come Dancing* contestant.

A Pressing Engagement

I feel slightly delicate this morning after yesterday's experience but soon rally when Miss Elizabeth – a white and tabby creature with knitting needle legs and a common voice – reverses up to my cage with the clear intention of piddling over the sheet that the EM has thoughtfully draped over one corner. Luckily, Master Wobble collides with her just at the crucial moment so that she loses her composure and counts herself fortunate not to have been crushed by that porky little body.

Daddy Uncle, as Poor Roger seems to be as far as I'm concerned, comes home early today and engages Wobble in conversation – or succeeds in getting him to stop eating for a few seconds, anyway.

'So what do you think of your little girlfriend, Benjy?' he asks. 'Isn't she pretty? Would you like her to stay and be your fiancée?'

A cold feeling grows in the pit of my stomach. It's nothing to do with Benjamin – one swipe round the chops should sort him out. No – the really terrifying thing is that I'm trapped in a house with two people who are as mad as each other when foolishly I'd clung to the belief that at least Daddy Uncle was just playing along with things for a quiet life. I'll have to speak to Blind Sammy about his escape plans and whether they could include a very small and pretty black cat who would look after him and act as his eyes – at least till we got out of the garden.

They're All Mad

Apparently, we're all excited because The Project has been completed and Master Benjamin will be able to go into the garden at the weekend. Last night the fat, pointy-faced badgers failed totally to comprehend the new arrangements for accessing the supper that was so tastefully slapped down for them on the paving stone by the summerhouse. Instead of coming in by the new back gate, which was propped open for them, they dug a new tunnel which would have comfortably accommodated Eurostar. Why anyone would be that bothered about reaching some dried-up cat food and cakes that could have made their own way to the rubbish tip quite defeats me, but then I'm a smoked salmon girl myself.

The Weekend

The patio door is open and Benjamin Wobble and Blind Sammy have lurched and stumbled into the garden. Don't mind me, anybody, stuck in this cage with a howling gale whistling round my nether regions!

The EM and Poor Roger are out there, aimlessly trailing after Benjamin, confident that Blind Sammy will be content to potter in the bushes. An hour later, Benjamin is back in and everybody suddenly realises that Blind Sammy hasn't been spotted for a very long time. One of the EM's most striking characteristics is the remarkable ability she has to go from being almost rational to complete off-the-wall panic within seconds.

Now one of Poor Roger's great successes has been attaching a Locator chip to Sammy's collar. This makes a bleeping noise and flashes when Poor Roger presses the right button on the Locator handset. Unfortunately, they can never find the handset, and today is no exception. Tensions are running high by the time the Locator is located in the medicine chest.

Armed with this invaluable tool, they rush madly round the garden for some time before anybody has the gumption to look over the fence into next door's garden where Sammy is strolling around without a care in the world. The EM zooms round to fetch him and returns with an unrepentant Sammy clutched to her heaving bosom.

Later I ask Sammy whether he has given up all hopes of escaping. 'Never!' he growls, 'they'll have to cut my claws up to my elbows before I give up!'

Within minutes, the EM has swooped on Sammy with the claw clippers and has done the deed. The language is dreadful – and Sammy's is pretty awful too.

'Did that hurt?' I ask him.

'Not at all,' he replies, having considered the matter to the point where I think he's gone back to sleep. 'But one has one's pride. The youngsters today don't understand about pride. Look at that Benjamin – he'll bonk anything that moves and practically everything that doesn't. And as for...'

Regular snoring confirms that the sentence will never be completed.

Out in the garden, Benjamin Wobble has found an ancient catnip toy and is rolling on it while Daddy Uncle smiles indulgently and the EM fights a losing battle to remove half a gallon of slimy green dribble from Wobble's coat.

Carloads of volunteers suddenly arrive and are invited in to peer at me. They seem harmless enough but are traumatised by the shock of seeing a normal cat in a household where most of them have bits missing or think that Victoria is still Queen of England. One of them asks if I've got four legs and whether I'm brain-damaged. I smile upon her – a thin-lipped smile which she should realise means I'll get her later.

Let Me Out!

I've trashed my cage, tipped the water bowl over and chucked half a ton of cat litter into the food dish. At 8 o'clock in the evening, they get the message and open the door of the cage. Yippee doo! Out I pop like the proverbial champagne cork while the EM and Poor Roger "ooh" and "aah" on the sofa. Wobble comes floundering after me and gets caught up in the wiring that snakes tastefully around the skirting board. 'Evie's like a tiny ballet dancer!' coos the EM, as I twirl and pirouette across the floor.

After an hour or so, I make an error of judgement and nip back into the cage for a snack. The old EM launches herself off the sofa with astonishing speed and slams the door shut, so I retire to my igloo for a good sulk.

CHAPTER TWO

Fun and Frolics

After numerous discussions, the EM and Poor Roger have decided to let me into the garden although they are still very worried that I might get "losted" and be "fritted". I've no idea why they talk like this. It's extremely embarrassing.

It's wonderful out here. There's a fountain thing down the bottom of the garden and I'm up on it in one leap, pulling faces at the birdies and splashing water over Miss Isabelle, who is lurking about below, no doubt hoping I'll drown myself. Bad luck, sister!

I think there might be woods beyond the fence but I've had enough excitement for one day. I'll just snatch that catnip toy away from Benjamin, then I think a little siesta might be in order.

Bad Badgers

A most unwelcome early morning disturbance occurs just as I'm concentrating on finding my missing jellybeans which must have slipped behind a cushion or stuck to the EM's trousers. Apparently, the silly bloody badgers have breached the barricades once again, so the EM is down there messing about with paving slabs and planks of wood. I wouldn't give much for old Brillo Badger's

9

chances of a cordon bleu platter this evening.

They finally dismantled the kitten pen last night, although I haven't been in it for a while now. It had become something of a feature and accumulated a whole population of magazines, worm pills and chocolate wrappers on its dipping roof. The EM had one of her friends round this afternoon and Miss Isabelle informs me that I missed a real treat when the EM absent-mindedly put down her tea cup on the roof of the pen, as she thought, only to realise it was no longer there when the cup crashed to the floor.

I return from a tough couple of hours of woodpecker taunting to find a porky ginger tail draped over the side of my igloo. I try poking at it but Wobble is obviously having some deeply absorbing – and probably extremely suspect – dream, because he refuses to stir. Never mind. A leap onto the roof produces the desired result in no time – out he flops with his legs in disarray and his fuzzy little dream shattered. Actually, I don't think I want to go in there now.

Springtime in the Cat Pens

An army of volunteers arrives to help the EM in the cat pens. These pens are where the waifs and strays while away their useless little lives until someone comes along and adopts them. I make it my business to pop round there at frequent intervals to pull faces at them and generally make them realise how needy and pathetic they are. Prancing about on the roof gives me particular pleasure as it drives them insane and often results in devoted couples who are viewing the cats having a major disagreement.

A volunteer called Maureen scoops up Wobble and fails to realise for a while that her jumper is beginning to bear an uncanny resemblance to a Marmite sandwich. I could have told her that dear little Benjy had just used the facilities and "fellded over" in a chocolate pudding, but some things people just have to find out for themselves.

It's not really Maureen's morning. Barely half an hour later, a bloodcurdling scream is heard from the direction of the pens and there's poor old Maureen, hyperventilating and clutching her neck. Apparently Sooty, who is no lightweight, fancied sitting on Maureen's shoulder and misjudged things, digging into Maureen's flesh to save herself. It shook Sooty up very badly and didn't seem to do much for Maureen, who suddenly remembered she should be somewhere else and left rather abruptly while the EM was still half-heartedly searching for the TCP.

With tensions running high indoors, I take myself off into the Wild Wood beyond the back fence. Benjamin can't trail after me, being totally unable to haul that fat little ginger body over a six-foot fence, so I can actually roll around in the leaves without being jumped on.

I've chummed up with some of the wild cats who seem to be a bit more switched on than Benjy and the Dollops. In fact, Spitfire – black, lean and mean – has become my role model. That cat knows more rude words than Ozzy Osbourne and doesn't care who she swears at, including foxes and the EM.

Spitfire is an expert pigeon fancier. Only a couple of days ago, the EM was peering up into the beech tree, trying to track down the source of a lot of squawking, when a half-dead pigeon plummeted at 100 miles an hour and hit her on the head. She dropped a tray of cat food destined for the waifs and lurched after the doomed pigeon while the rest of us watched in dismay. Suddenly, a black flash streaked past the EM, grabbed the pigeon, broke its neck and started eating it. She looked up with blood and feathers all round her mouth – Spitfire, I mean, not the EM.

Then there's Delilah, who is a bit dim but smart enough to know she's landed on her rather pretty tortoiseshell paws. Delilah has long fur and is often seen with half the garden in her knickers. When she first came here, she went into the Wild Wood and was totally unable to find her way back again, according to Miss Isabelle. Delilah kept screaming and in the end the EM convinced herself that old fuzzy knickers was caught in a trap so she went to look for her. After an hour or so of being bitten to death by mosquitoes and wrenching her ankles in badger holes, the EM realised the noise was moving around and returned home in high dudgeon, whatever that might be.

Dennis is an ancient tabby feral who comes from a long line of wildcats, so if there is such a thing as a pedigree feral, then Dennis is one. He was trapped by Cats Protection volunteers as a kitten in the grounds of the local mental hospital when that worthy institution was about to be demolished to make way for about five million new homes. Dennis was only a few weeks old when he fell into the EM's clutches, but after 15 years he's as wild as can be – and that's pretty damn wild, I can tell you. In fact, sometimes Dennis is so angry that his little body shakes with emotion and he has to have a catnip fix to calm him down.

Skippy has been here for years as well. He was named after that ridiculous kangaroo that kept rushing about all over the place and always knew when the water level was rising. Now Skippy can take or leave water levels but does a lot of rushing. He's particularly noted for rushing indoors and stealing food, then dribbling it all over the floor and causing certain people to nearly break their silly necks. He has even been known to go in the bedroom and snatch a power nap on the bed, spitting and growling at the EM and Poor Roger when they retire for the night.

The fifth feral is a cat that I feel it is my duty to bully – a cat no better than she should be, who was found in a car park in Woking with five wretched babies. Has the animal no pride? Did she have to fling herself into the trap just because she was starving? Anyway, her ghastly babies have all been homed now to vulnerable people who would have agreed to anything to get away from the EM, and we're stuck with dear little Pansy who likes nothing better than to roll around in the grass with Benjamin Wobble. And yes, I know I don't want him but I don't want her to have him either. Nothing unreasonable about that, I would have thought.

Another Day, Another Crisis

Great excitement! The EM has staggered back from the vet's with the most enormous tomcat – about twice the size of Benjamin and with very noticeable tail end trimmings. "Harold" is decanted into the pen and sits in the dirt tray, scowling out at the world in general and the EM in particular.

Miss Elizabeth and I fall over each other in our haste to make his acquaintance but he doesn't seem over impressed. The ginger glove puppet wobbles past and nearly has a heart attack when Harold launches himself at the wire.

At teatime, the EM ventures into Harold's pen with what she obviously thinks is every tomcat's dream meal but his reaction confirms that once again our "expert" has got it wrong. Chicken Kittydins hasn't quite hit the mark, we gather as a striped paw the size of a soup plate smacks the jolly red dish out of the EM's grasp. There probably are more amusing things than seeing her crawling about on the floor of the pen with a menacing tabby threatening to leap on her back, but this will do for now.

Progress?

Why do I feel this will end in tears? On the face of things, the EM has made great progress with Harold who hasn't smacked the food out of her hand for a while. He's been "adjusted" and seems a quieter and more thoughtful cat – and considerably less interesting, if you want to know.

Miss Elizabeth and I accompany the EM on her evening rounds. She's just gone in with Harold, who is looking at her in a strange and dreamy kind of way. She extends a shaky hand and lets him rub his great jowls against it.

'That's so much better, Harold!' she squeaks, 'I knew you were a lovely boy really!'

The last few words of this moving utterance are almost lost in a flurry of claws and fur as Harold leaps on to the

EM's back and hangs on, purring in a deeply unnerving manner. This is bad news. Very bad news. Harold has fallen deeply in love with the EM and not in a good way, but in an "I-want-you-all-to-myself" kind of way that cats are not supposed to do.

Miss Elizabeth reports subsequently that the EM's back is "a right mess" and the T-shirt has been consigned to the cat bed box. What a cheek! What self-respecting feline is going to want some ripped reject covered in blood? Later I hear a mumbled conversation between the EM and one of her cronies which ends with the EM in an emotional state (as she is most days after the second glass of El Plonko).

'I suppose you're right,' she snuffles, 'I'm sure he'll get a good home there. It's just that I feel such a traitor because he's put his trust in me!'

I resist an urge to vomit. Any cat daft enough to put his trust in anything as dodgy as the EM deserves all he gets, and it sounds like old Harold's in for a rude awakening.

Summertime, and the Living Isn't Easy

Well, we could have sold tickets to watch the EM trying to bang Harold up in the cat carrier. For a start, she keeps snivelling, so just as there might have been a remote possibility of grabbing the great lump and ramming him into the carrier, the EM goes all misty and can't see a thing. The other problem is that Harold's devotion has taken a bit of a knock and he's quite keen on taking the EM's face off.

Miss Isabelle and I are sitting in the bushes in a quietly

supportive way when the EM's friend comes windmilling round the corner and frightens us nearly to death. (Note for diary: get friend when she's least expecting it.)

This coincides with Harold raking his great claws across the EM's knuckles. It's the sort of moment when getting on a one-way spaceship seems a really attractive idea. The friend scampers off indoors and returns with a handful of Kleenex tissues which she proceeds to thread through the wire of the pen and the EM dabs at the blood which is fairly pulsing out of her podgy hand.

Instead of abandoning the enterprise, the EM is galvanised by Harold's treachery and has him banged up in the carrier in no time. She's even stopped snuffling and they set off in a far more cheerful frame of mind than could have been anticipated a few moments previously.

I gather Harold is being transferred to a large rescue centre where he will be tended by a whole team of people to avoid what has been described as "inappropriate and excessive bonding". Miss Isabelle and I ponder the merits of taking a trip down there, but in the end decide to settle for the devil we know rather than risk being cared for by people who actually know what they're doing.

When the EM returns, she wastes no time in cleaning out Harold's pen ready for the next waif, who is apparently arriving tomorrow. This one's called Charlie and he has suffered some emotional damage. Who hasn't, I'd like to know! What do people think it's like living with an over-sexed, ginger pumpkin, two mad humans and a cast of feline misfits?

CHAPTER THREE

Holidays and Other Horror Stories

The EM is typing away dementedly this morning – with the help of the ancient and faded tortoiseshell, Joan Collins. This old bags of bones is at least 21 years old and spends her time reminiscing about past theatrical triumphs when she's not snoring her head off in the wardrobe. All goes well until Joan scampers across the keyboard in pursuit of a juicy bluebottle and the EM's priceless prose disappears into the ether.

Eventually, a fistful of papers emerge which we assume must be the EM's latest doomed attempt to complete yet another "distance learning" writing course. The distance between the EM and any possibility of learning anything is vast and one's sympathy goes out to those poor souls who have to wade through pages of *"What Benjy Did Next"*, or some such drivel.

Minutes later, Miss Isabelle bounds in to report disturbing goings-on in the bedroom. No – nothing like that; it's something far more worrying – the appearance of a suitcase. It appears that the EM has been hunched over the keyboard writing a resumé of our requirements for the person who will be looking after us while they skip off on holiday. Me, me, me, me, me!! Not a thought in her head for anybody else!

Within a remarkably short space of time they've flung

a few ancient items of clothing into the case, had a row about not being able to find the mobile phone charger and departed – but not before we've all been subjected to enough slobbery kisses to last several lifetimes. The wild cats have got the right idea, skulking about down the garden where the EM and Poor Roger can't get their hands on them, but even they don't escape completely. Delilah manages an impressive yawn as the EM waves and blows kisses from the patio, and Skippy sprays over the bushes to show how upset he is about their impending absence.

As the tin box clatters off into the distance, we give a collective sigh of relief and crash out. It's only a couple of hours later that we begin to wonder what will happen at suppertime, and another hour after that we all begin to feel rather fond of the dear old EM and Poor Roger.

We are rudely awakened by the door being flung open and a cheery voice calling our names. This takes some time as there are 15 of us, and by the time she's drawn breath I have recognised who the voice belongs to. It is none other than the traitor who brought me down here in the dark days of the New Year. I suppose this is the EM's idea of a joke. They have left us to the mercies of this woman while they go off enjoying themselves.

"Auntie K" settles down to read through the EM's epic which apparently details not only who has what and when, but what to say to the neighbours in the unlikely event that one of them should feel strong enough to ask about us. The EM has always been numerically challenged – or perhaps just finds it hard to face the truth – and has never been able to confess to the neighbours just how many of us there are on the home team.

"Rounding down" is achieved by Skippy and Miss Elizabeth being the same cat; Dennis, Bun-Bun and Cleo are also the same cat and Pansy and Isabelle likewise. Spitfire and I are the same cat, and Delilah could be Katya if she has to be. Even if Skippy and Miss Elizabeth, for example, should appear at the same time, the EM will brazen it out, claiming that it's a trick of the light or that one of them is a spaniel and it's an easy mistake to make. By the time the listener has grappled with all of this, he or she is generally only too thankful to glug back a tumbler of El Plonko and stumble away.

That leaves Benjamin Wobble and Blind Sammy who are at least both ginger, Joan Collins, who could never be anyone other than herself, and Miss Portia Patch, who is probably a very small person dressed up as a cat.

Should Auntie K fail to grasp these nuances if presented with a challenge, she is exhorted to say that any cat mentioned definitely doesn't live here and how fed up she is with all these cats coming into the garden when they have a perfectly good home at that house in the woods.

It Could be Worse

Have had to revise my view of Auntie K who let me stay up very late last night while she sat outside on badger watch. It was gone midnight when the fat, pointy-faced spongers turned up, rooting about amongst the leftovers, before loping round the garden and ripping up the grass just to show they would rather eat worms any day of the week.

This morning she's up early – not loafing about in bed till six in the morning like some I could mention – and goes straight down to close off the badger tunnel so that Benjamin and Sammy won't get "losted" in the woods. Or wouldn't if they ever managed to get off the sofa. Auntie K is being very nice to me, saying things like, 'You're a proper cat, Evie, and you don't get too many of those to the pound round here!' I have therefore decided not to kill her – for the time being, anyway.

Sammy is planning to break out sometime later today, so we'll see how our minder copes with that little crisis. He thinks his claws have grown long enough to haul himself over the fence behind the summerhouse and he plans to pull off his collar with its telltale bleeper so that nobody will be able to track him down. I mention the small matter of starving to death, as not being able to see could make hunting a bit tricky, but he just rambles on about the spirit that won the war and goes back to sleep.

A few hours have passed and Auntie K has rushed through the patio door, clutching Sammy's collar – without Sammy being attached to it, I mean. 'Here's the bleeping collar but we've lost the bleeping cat!' she rants. 'Who saw him go? It'll be dark soon! We'll never find him!'

A couple of us half wake up. We're so used to this kind of irrational outburst that I quite think the EM has come back prematurely. Auntie K is flapping round the garden and Benjamin Wobble has decided to "helpit" her which could well push the poor woman over the brink. I decide to wander into the spare room where I think I left the remains of my mouse under the duvet and there, sleeping the sleep of the innocent, is Blind Sammy, curled up in a dirt tray.

A quick poke of the paw soon has him snuffling and gulping and lurching to his feet. Apparently he turned the wrong way at the lounge door – a fatal flaw in his escape plan, I fear, but Auntie K is so thrilled to see the old fool that he is given all sorts of goodies and told that he's been a very brave old soldier. Not quite the words I would have used myself, but there we are.

Boredom Redefined

The last few days have actually passed quite pleasantly, but a huge commotion this morning announced the return of our intrepid travellers, who have, it turns out, been on a four day cruise up and down the Channel. And are we going to hear about it!

Once the kissing and cuddling has abated slightly, those of us who can get over the fence into the woods make a mad dash for it, leaving Benjamin and Sammy to help with the unpacking and generally be bored rigid with the EM's oh-so-amusing accounts of life on the ocean wave. I think there may have been a couple of hours when they actually couldn't see any land. The EM keeps quoting lines from *The Rime of the Ancient Mariner* and I can see some relevance. That bit about the glittering eye with its undertones of madness is particularly appropriate.

The day starts pleasantly enough, with the EM trundling out into the back garden to make sure that the latest inhabitant of the rescue pens hasn't escaped. This is unlikely as she would have needed explosives, wire cutters and a forged vaccination certificate to reach freedom.

I run down with the EM to have a good look at the dismal wretch and to encourage her by pulling faces. As usual, the EM misinterprets this as sisterly concern.

'Don't worry, Evie,' she coos, 'nobody's going to hurt her. We're going to see how tame she is and if she's a good girl we'll be able to find her a nice home.'

With that, little black Purrdie takes a swipe at the EM's podgy fingers and knocks the bowl of goodies all over the floor.

Around 10 o'clock, there are sinister developments. The EM keeps peering into cupboards and dark corners and ticking things off on a long list. She begins to hum tunelessly – always a bad sign – and shuts the patio door in a purposeful manner. I immediately fling myself against it, howling dementedly, and she lets me out – but not before she's looked over her shoulder to see who else might be making a run for it.

Miss Isabelle told me what happened later. Apparently, two very brisk and efficient ladies turned up, carrying a big black case stuffed full of torture implements and the EM welcomed them like long-lost friends. After all sorts of jolly exchanges, the EM swooped on poor Isabelle and hoisted her up on the table for that awful thing termed a "booster jab". After the needle had penetrated every muscle in her body, Miss Isabelle was beside herself and felt the need to piddle on the tablecloth (the dining room table having been commandeered as the field hospital) but this didn't stop the Chief Torturer, who then decided to look at Miss Isabelle's teeth. She was just saying that they had a lot of tartar on them when Isabelle crunched into her hand and leapt out of her clutches.

Miss Elizabeth was next up and purred throughout in an ingratiating way, so Miss Isabelle is planning to kill her. Joan Collins gave a good account of herself before disappearing back into the depths of the wardrobe, but Cleo was a spent force, having already savaged the EM as a result of an earlier misunderstanding about a pink pill. Miss Isabelle said she almost felt sorry for the humans when it was time to examine Master Benjamin Wobble, as the great porky lump wanted to kiss everybody and kept rolling about on the table like a fur-covered skittle. Apparently his teeth are disgusting, which confirms what a good decision it was not to let him share my igloo.

By the time they had worked their way through the list, Miss Isabelle said they were all worn out and the humans had hands like underground maps.

CHAPTER FOUR

Bad Behaviour

It is 8pm and the EM and Poor Roger are whirling around, snatching up cat bowls as if they feared a predatory tiger might appear in the kitchen any second. Even the dishes outside have disappeared, I now notice.

My own dish is, of course, in the middle of the dining room table so that I can enjoy the extensive views of next door's garage wall and the half dead rose that from time to time attempts to scramble up it before sinking back in a heap of blighted petals. Observing that the others are starving as the night advances and knowing they can't get up on the table, I make sure I give my remaining biscuits a good old poke and crunch. This drives Lizzie wild to the point where she slaps Isabelle, who crashes into Blind Sammy. Pandemonium breaks out in the most satisfactory way.

Morning edges its cautious way into Tresta Towers and the familiar sounds of the EM crashing into the wardrobe door intrude on a rather pleasant dream about a squirrel nipping Benjamin's nose. Anybody with any sense would know that it's not a good idea to put a plastic cat dish on a wooden floor – anybody apart from the EM, that is.

An hour passes and there is still no sign of any food. The mood is mutinous and Cleo achieves cult hero status by lashing out at the EM as she attempts to pass between the worktop and the door. Poor Roger departs for work, seeming a tad keener than usual, and the EM locks herself in the bathroom.

An hour passes and the EM emerges. She rushes through the bungalow, to reappear with something that looks ominously like a cat carrier. We all suddenly realise we have pressing business at the bottom of the garden – all except Master Benjamin, who can't wait to fling his silly ginger body into it.

'It's a trap, you fool!' I mutter as I rush to the door, but he can't be saved. Moving with frightening speed, the EM whisks him into the car. Luckily, she has the sense to whisk back in and feed us before screeching off with poor Benjamin. I wonder if we'll ever see him again? Oh well, if we don't, we don't. I can't worry about it.

I fear the worst. She's back and there's no sign of the ginger dollop. Poor Roger keeps phoning all morning and the EM says things like, 'They won't have started on him yet. I'll ring you when there's any news.'

A crony of the EM's phones and all is revealed. 'Yes – he's there now,' says the EM in her tense voice. 'We've had to go for it. His teeth are in a terrible state!'

So all that drama and the wretched cat's just having a few teeth out! I thought he must be having a triple bypass, the way the EM was behaving. And as for Poor Roger! Of course, the EM's a bit miffed because when she had a minor adjustment recently, Poor Roger came home from work and only remembered she was waiting to be collected from the day ward after a relaxing hour spent poking pine needles out of the spouts on the fountain.

It's mid-afternoon and Master Benjamin is home, sporting a rather trendy green bandage on his leg. We've all got to keep quiet, apparently, because "poor baby's been very fritted and needs to rest". The next thing we hear is the familiar crashing of food bowls as our little invalid swims through half a kilo of Kittydins and staggers off wearing most of it.

The EM is twittering on about the Tooth Furry. 'I wonder what the Tooth Furry will leave under Benjy Boo's pillow tonight?' she coos. 'It might be a pouch of his favourite goodies!' Dream on, chicken. When I last looked under Benjie Boo's pillow, there was a lump of dried moss, a few tail feathers and an unidentifiable brown lump.

Enter Miss Betty

I am just enjoying an afternoon nap on my turtle-shaped cushion when the most awful yowling sound assails my delicate little eardrums. I find myself envying the ancient residents who wouldn't notice a bomb exploding in the back garden as the EM lurches through the lounge, holding a cat carrier aloft. At first I think the carrier is empty and wonder if the EM has perfected a rather novel ventriloquist act, but as she draws closer I notice that it contains a spider-like tabby blob with a mouth the size of a moon crater.

'Say "hello" to Betty, everybody,' trills the EM. 'Poor Betty's had a terrible time and we must all be kind to her.'

By now, the ever-charitable tabby, Cleo, has roused herself. 'It would be a kindness to put the thing out of its misery,' she hisses sweetly, 'and I'm willing to do it myself if the rest of you are feeling squeamish!'

There is a collective sigh of relief as the EM speeds across the garden in the direction of the summerhouse where Betty will reside until some vulnerable person can be prevailed upon to take the wretched thing away. Master Benjamin Wobble positions himself outside the summerhouse door, already in love with anything that has such an impressive range of expletives at its command.

It is nearly midnight and the noise coming from the summerhouse has finally stopped, but we're all on edge as we're just waiting for Betty to start up again. Betty is about six inches long and we could hear her with the summerhouse door shut and the patio door barricaded. Even when she was eating, we could hear her, although that mush she was wading through would silence most things.

The EM says she's suffering from Tourette's Syndrome and can't help herself – Betty, I mean, not the EM – although now I come to think of it… We get quite a few spirited outbursts around here. Only the other day, Poor Roger was carrying out his duties round by the cat pens and dropped an enormous bag of cat litter, which exploded over the garden. This was closely followed by a visiting friend nearly braining himself on the corner of the pen roof. In each case, the range of curses was impressive and we gave thanks – not for the first time – that our elderly neighbour is hard of hearing.

In the morning, Betty can be heard out-chirruping the dawn chorus. Miss Isabelle claims not to have slept a wink and Sammy says the noise reminded him of the trenches in the Great War. Even the EM's relentless morning cheerfulness seems a trifle muted as she totters out with the breakfast tray and copious supplies of kitchen roll.

'Oh, how wonderful! What a clever little girl you are, Betty Boo! You are sooooo clever! Auntie could eat you up!'

For goodness' sake! Whatever has the kitten done? Recited the Theory of Relativity? Covered the walls of the summerhouse with Andy Warhol-type paintings of cat food tins? No. What Betty has achieved, gentle reader, is two very small firm poos which are almost in the dirt tray. As I may have observed before, it takes very little to make the EM happy.

Heartening though this news is, I begin to fear that Betty might hang around a bit as there are dangerous signs of bonding going on down the garden. Poor Roger is similarly besotted, referring to the ugly thing as a "poor little mite", which she obviously isn't. That kitten is a control freak, if ever I saw one. Because she makes so much noise when she's left on her own, she's been given a teddy bear, a transistor radio and a brand new bed. Just give her a mobile phone and a laptop, why don't you!

It is evening on Day Two of the Reign of the Screamer. We are on our little furry knees – not just because of the noise, but because we're absolutely sick of hearing about what a terrible time little Betty has had. Apparently someone took her to the vet's and demanded to have her put to sleep. Well, if you hadn't slept for two months, you would feel pretty desperate, wouldn't you? I've only missed a few hours and I could cheerfully shove Betty's little tabby head under the algae infested waters of the fountain.

Anyway, just as we are wondering what to do about ASBO kitten, who should magic up but our friend, Auntie K, who looked after us when we were abandoned earlier this year. Within minutes, ASBO Betty is spirited away to be fostered in her house up the road. Auntie K plans to put her in the bathroom. No, I want to scream, don't do that! Her yowling will echo all round the house to the point where Barry the bunny will wish he was slumbering in a pie dish and Doris the parrot will find herself out-parroted by a tabby-coloured foghorn.

Bring On the Weirdos

The EM is in her element, moaning non-stop about how busy she is and how it's a pity some other people don't get off their backsides and do something to help. According to Miss Isabelle, the roads of downtown Woking are littered with the bodies of those who have offered to help but have lacked the stamina required to sustain their enthusiasm confronted by the EM in her "Martyr of the Year" role.

The first glass of El Plonko has gone down without touching the sides. Before the EM can replenish her glass, a car crawls into the drive and four large human puddings erupt onto the concrete. Four smaller puddings then emerge and tear across the front garden, each carrying what looks horribly like a kitten.

The EM is out through the door like a rather bulky bat. 'May I ask what you think you're doing?' she bawls in a voice that would halt the migration of the wildebeests.

'You said to bring the kittens to you. Well, here we are – the kids have got them.'

I think for a moment that the EM is going to explode, but instead she launches herself at the galloping brats and grabs the kittens. By the time she's finished, the puddings are considerably sadder but not necessarily wiser. It was when the parents asked her how much money she would give them for the kittens that I thought the old EM's eyes would pop out.

'Money?' she screamed, 'money? Have you any idea how much it's going to cost us to get these kittens sorted out, or hadn't you noticed they can hardly breathe or open their eyes?'

Deep joy! The sickly kittens are in the isolation pen, although Benjamin is desperate to make contact, attracted as he always is by nasal discharges and squitty bottoms. The EM is busy mixing up all sorts of stuff in the kitchen and I realise that our supper is but a distant mirage. Poor Roger is surreptitiously looking up the closing times of the local takeaways and even the El Plonko bottle has a strangely neglected look.

The kittens seem jolly little things, considering they are so sickly, and readily submit to the EM syringing stuff down their throats. They consume large quantities of food, which pass rapidly through them and re-appear over the floor, over each other and over the EM.

The next morning finds everybody still in the land of the living, although I have to look twice at the EM to check this out. The four poorly kittens are whisked off to the vet's to be sorted out and thankfully are kept in to be rehydrated – whatever that might be.

No sooner has the EM returned and crunched her way through a handful of coffee granules, than a man arrives with a rather exotic-looking cat. Gazing at that plush cream coat and elfin face, I experience a strong desire to poke her eyes out.

I regret to say, however, that the language issuing forth from this vision of loveliness is on the gutter side of coarse. Benjamin Wobble, Isabelle and I gather round the pen while the EM encourages Griselda to come out of the carrier. In the end, the EM decides to leave her in there to emerge in her own time, but not before this bitch cat from hell has extended a chocolate-coloured paw to swipe the EM's ankle.

The owner grins apologetically, having no doubt perfected this technique after years of living with old Grizzles. 'She's always been an indoor cat. She's probably terrified of all the noises,' he simpers. 'I'm sure once she realises she's safe, she'll be absolutely fine.'

Predictably, the EM embarks on her "If-I-had-£10-for-every-time-I've-heard-that" speech and I catch Isabelle mouthing along to it, which gives me a good excuse to smack her one.

The erstwhile owner signs his beloved cat into the EM's tender care without so much as a backward glance and fairly skips back to the car, promising a donation to follow. The EM said that would be very nice in the sort of tone that implied she expected to see a pig fly past any minute.

The snuffly kittens return in the afternoon. Apparently, various poo samples have been harvested and are being sent off to the laboratory. What a delight it must be to work in such a place! You certainly wouldn't want to discuss your day over a chicken vindaloo, would you? Imagine being reprimanded for some misdeed. "You're in deep shit, now, Carruthers," your superior would growl. "No change there then," you'd quip, in a desperate attempt to lighten the mood.

Against the odds, we've made it through to the evening and Poor Roger staggers home from work to be regaled with tales of dark deeds and runny bottoms.

The EM has prepared a special supper in an effort to win old Grizzles over and we amble round with her. The good news is that Grizzles has emerged from her carrier; the bad news is that she's standing there, growling and spitting at the EM. A sudden swipe sees the EM drop the food, step in the water bowl and hit her elbow on a wooden shelf. Game, set and match to Grizzles.

CHAPTER FIVE

Cometh the Saint, Cometh the Sucker

The days have passed and several vet appointments have been made for Griselda. It's not that she's ill, but the EM had planned to take her to have her checked over and to have those awful things that are supposed to stop you being ill but actually nearly kill you. The EM always says they're nothing to worry about. Yeah, right.

Anyway, Griselda has decided she doesn't want to go to the vet's, so the appointments have had to be cancelled or sometimes another poor creature's been wheeled out instead so the EM can save face. Griselda's decision not to go to the vet's has manifested itself in the form of snarling and leaping at the EM's face in a really quite unpleasant way, although Benjamin is fascinated by it and thinks he is in love with Grizzles. If he really believes that a quick bonk will cheer her up, I fear he may be piddling up the wrong bush – again.

Of course, the most worrying thing of all is how we will ever get shot of her, because there is a worrying tendency for anyone who can't get a home to stay here – except for me, of course. Everybody wanted little Evie but the EM just couldn't imagine life without me.

The EM has just emerged from the cupboard they laughingly refer to as "The Study" with a broad grin on her melon-like face. She's either got indigestion or has managed to stitch up some vulnerable person.

Apparently, she's received an e-mail from someone who wants an indoor cat. She's spoken to them on the phone and at some point in the conversation suddenly realised that "Terry" was, in fact, "Terry" – in other words, some unfortunate creature that she used to work with years ago. By then the poor mutt was already in it up to his neck and didn't stand a chance.

It is the following evening and Terry and Mrs Terry have come to visit Griselda.

Mrs Terry begins to smell a rat when the EM bars her way to the door of the pen.

Wedging her short but substantial frame against the mesh, the EM clears her throat and launches into an embarrassingly emotional account of Griselda's troubles.

'You wouldn't believe what this poor cat has been through,' she intones, with a Princess Diana-like flutter. 'I really don't think she's ever experienced love. The previous owner couldn't get away quick enough. Just dumped her and ran.'

I am prowling about on the roof of Grizzle's pen and choose that moment to hang over the edge like a rather glamorous beanie baby.

'And that cat's not helping either!' snaps the EM, flapping a hand in my direction. 'Buzz off, Evie!'

Buzz off! I think not, Madam! If I want to hang over and pull faces at Old Chocolate Paws I will, thank you!

Terry has tears in his eyes. 'I hate to think about animals not being loved,' he mumbles. 'There's no excuse for it. She looks a lovely girl, doesn't she, darling?'

"Darling" obviously isn't quite such a soft touch as hubby and is desperate to get inside that pen. 'Yes, she does, but I'd still like to go in and see her, please.'

I sometimes think I underestimate the old EM. She's not very bright but is possessed of a certain low cunning.

'Of course you can!' she coos, leaping away from the door. 'You go in and talk to her. Just stand back a bit because she's still very frightened and we wouldn't want to upset her, would we? I think she'd been shut in a very small room for long periods of time, so being in the cat pen is very stressful for her.'

Mrs Terry clutches at her throat. 'Shut in a small room?' she quivers. 'Oh no – that's terrible. That happened to me when I was a child and it took me years to get over!'

'Sometimes, I don't think you're quite over it yet, my darling,' contributes Terry helpfully.

Scenting victory, the EM is now positively urging Mrs Terry to enter the lion's den, but the poor woman is at the mercy of her memories and has decided that there is no need to go in because she has made her mind up. She and Mr Terry will give dear Griselda the best home she could ever have and will love her till hell freezes over.

As they depart in an excess of emotion, the EM shrugs and reaches for the El Plonko. She even tickles my ears – a sure sign that all is forgiven.

Special Delivery

The appointed day has arrived and the EM is slurping back an extra strong coffee before venturing into Griselda's pen to bang her up and transport her to Mr and Mrs Terry. She is visibly trembling as she bolts the door on the inside and approaches Grizzles, who is crouching in the corner of her house, her ears flattened in a most engaging manner.

The EM wafts a towel at her while manoeuvring a cat carrier through the door, then wafts it out again after Grizzles has ripped it to shreds. Poor Roger eventually comes out to ask our red-faced heroine how things are going. Luckily, she is so breathless that all she can manage is a feeble, 'What's it look like?' and Poor Roger shuffles back indoors.

At some point old Grizzles' concentration must have lapsed – and it may be that I can claim some credit for that as a dangling beanie baby can be a bit of a distraction – because somehow she ends up in the carrier and is transported off to her new home.

Sound Bites

Two weeks have passed and apparently, Griselda is settling in beautifully. She is only biting Mr Terry a few times a day now and the course of antibiotics seems to be working well. So well, in fact, that only one of his arms now looks as if it belonged to Henry VIII; the other one has gone down to just twice its normal size.

Mrs Terry is besotted with Grizzles, who has obviously realised who opens her Kittydins. This comes as a huge relief to all of us because it means the old bitch won't be coming back.

Just as everybody is relaxing, the phone decides to ring in a particularly menacing manner. Miss Elizabeth says I have an overactive imagination and that the phone always makes the same noise, but she's not sensitive.

Anyway, even old Lizzie is forced to reconsider when she hears the EM's voice rising.

'Ripped your leg through the bars of the trap? Broke the door of the crusher cage? Would I collect him from the vet? And do what, exactly?'

It would seem that the unfortunate caller is one of the EM's colleagues from Cats Protection and that she has been involved in trapping a rather uncouth stray. On her way to the vet's, the ungrateful creature has apparently made his feelings known by reaching through the bars of the trap and mauling the poor woman's leg.

An hour later we're peeping out from behind the curtains as the EM pulls into the drive. She drags a cat trap off the back seat – a cat trap containing the biggest and most miserable-looking cat I've ever seen. Frank is pure white with piercing blue eyes and is making spirited efforts to savage the EM, who must be very thankful she went for the heavy-duty lumberjack jeans rather than the flimsier feminine variety, even though the diamante trimming did take her fancy.

Luckily, Frank is still slightly woozy from his "adjustment" and the hefty dose of anaesthetic he received. Unluckily, there are no pens available to decant Frank into. The EM, in an inspired move, decides to put old Frank into a kitten cage in the garage until a pen is available.

The garage door closes behind her and Frank. The noises are very worrying, particularly as we can't tell who is making them. There is some heavy duty grunting, followed by growling and swearing, then a terrible thud. Supposing Frank has shoved the EM in the cage! Who will open the door? Will it be the EM, weary but triumphant, or Frank, nonchalantly removing a scrap of the EM's clothing from his teeth?

At last the door opens and the EM staggers out, gasping. She smells terrible and there is a stream of amber fluid meandering down her plump face. 'The bugger sprayed all over me!' she snorts. 'I'll need more than that flaming Orchid Dew facewash to get rid of this pong!'

Frank Goes to Earth

It's all been going swimmingly. Frank has spent the last couple of days sulking at the back of the kitten pen and the EM has been poking food in at regular intervals. She has even managed to extract the dirt tray – complete with puddings that wouldn't have disgraced an Irish Wolfhound – without losing a single digit in the process.

Today we have the joyous news that a cat pen is available for Frank, so the EM is just going to pop into the garage and bundle him into a cat carrier. She is breezily confident as she disappears into the garage, and a complete wreck when she emerges some time later.

"He seems a nice cat," she had been heard to remark a day or two ago, "just frightened, that's all." This cosily optimistic view seems slightly at odds with the venom now spewing from her cherry lips as she slams the door and staggers to the sofa.

'That oversized snowflake's got it coming!' she snorts. 'Bloody well went for me when I reached in to get him! He needn't think I'm beaten – I just need to work out a plan.'

After several more doomed attempts to get old Frank out of the cage, the EM's master plan is unveiled. It is mind-blowing in its simplicity. She will open the door of the pen

Bella

Benjamin Wobble

Blind Sammy

Bonnie Bun Bun

Boris

Cleo

Delilah

Elizabeth

Evie

Isabelle

Kittens

Spitfire

Portia Patch

Pansy

Lucio

and let Frank out into the garage. She will then set the trap in the garage, Frank will go into it and all will be well.

Four days have gone by and there is no sign of Frank, in or out of the trap. A huge toad had been foolish enough to trigger the thing and was sitting forlornly amongst the remains of the Kittydins bait when the EM investigated this morning. Of course, toads are slightly limited in the facial expressions department, so that may just have been its normal look.

A further disappointment has been the discovery that Old Blue Eyes has been feasting on biscuits, having ripped the bag open with his horrible claws, so he's not the slightest bit bothered about the yummy bait the EM has been stuffing in the trap every night.

'I've got it! We'll soon have that cat sorted!' cries the EM suddenly and worryingly as we're all dozing away on a grey Sunday afternoon. Poor Roger latches on to the word "we" and starts coughing in case he needs to plead illness at any stage in the plan, and Benjamin Wobble, who is spread across Roger's lap, slides slowly and inevitably onto the floor.

'Frank's obviously hiding under a load of old rubbish in the garage, so the first thing will be to flush him out. Once he's in the open, we'll need two people in the garage. One to stop him running for cover and one to catch hold of him. Obviously, I'll be one of them...'

The colour has drained from Poor Roger's face and his cough has escalated from a mild irritation to a life-threatening bronchial spasm.

'Steve! That's who we need. I'll ring him now.'

Poor Roger recovers sufficiently to restore the still-sleeping Benjamin to his lap and to wonder if a cup of tea might be forthcoming.

It is evening and the lights are blazing cheerfully in the garage. The EM and Uncle Steve have been in there a while now and the only sounds we've heard have been muffled expletives as the EM and Uncle bounce off each other in the confined space.

I am beginning to think I might trot away and catch a pigeon when the EM's shrill and panicky voice is heard.

'To you! To you! He's on the run! Oh, my God – he's coming this way! Grab him! Get hold of him – now!'

There is a brief interlude of silence, then Steve shouts, 'He's bitten me! The bugger's bitten through my thumb!'

Sympathetic as always to the needs of others, the EM screams, 'Well, don't let go! Shove him in the carrier!'

Seconds later, the door is flung open triumphantly and the EM emerges, followed by Uncle Steve, who is lugging a red and white cat. Miss Elizabeth is clutching at her chest in a gesture worthy of a rather furry Puccini heroine, because she claims that any excitement is bad for her heart. Since the vet mentioned a flapping valve we've all had to be nice to the old bitch, when what she really needs is a good poke in the eye.

Luckily, the blood which has transformed poor old Frank into Dracula's companion animal turns out to be Uncle Steve's.

Bambi Meets Godzilla

Days have gone by and old Frank has got things all his own way. The EM looks like a particularly bizarre beekeeper when she goes in with his meals – that improvised veil draped over a Bob the Builder hard hat and the tent-like coat flapping round the ankles are enough to frighten me, anyway. Our hero has had a few perfunctory swipes at her, just to keep his paw in, and tends to loom over her when she's sorting out his dirt tray, which has resulted in much spillage.

We are rudely interrupted at supper-time by the arrival of a glamorous young woman who has come to view the cats. Benjamin immediately rolls over at her feet, leaving very little to the imagination, and the EM feels the need to excuse his exhibitionist tendencies by alluding to brain damage. My own view is that there was very little brain to start with, but then I'm not his mother, thank God.

Out we all troop to the pens to view the waifs, who are doing their best to look beguiling. All except Frank, of course, who couldn't care less and remains in the corner of his cat house like a sulky white lion.

'Oooh!' exclaims our guest, 'what a wonderful cat!'

Amazingly, she wasn't looking at me but at Old Blue Eyes. 'Can I go in and see him?'

We hold our breath as this slip of a girl enters the lion's den. Minutes pass and she's still in there, exchanging prolonged blinks with Frank. The EM has already explained that Frank needs an indoor home because he has something horrible called Feline Aids and mustn't give it to other cats.

'I'd love to have him,' says Girlie, 'I need to have an indoor cat where I live and Frank is just perfect.'

CHAPTER SIX

Pussycats and Parasites

The EM's shrill tones break into a rather pleasant dream I'm having about a robin flying into my mouth. *'Sammy! Sammy! Whatever do you think you're doing?'*

When I drag myself into the kitchen, it's perfectly obvious that Sammy is stuffing down the Wicked Biscuits as fast as he can go.

'Those are not your biscuits, Samuel,' whines the EM in her disappointed voice. 'You know what happens when you eat those – they come straight up again...'

Naughty Tortie

Up to now, Miss Portia Patch has kept as low a profile as is possible for a bulky tortoiseshell with bow legs. She did steal Miss Bonnie Bun-Bun's bed, but as the ancient tabby coat-hanger had abandoned it in favour of the EM's bed, she was hardly arguing from a position of strength.

If anybody is entitled to feel aggrieved, it is me, as for many months I enjoyed the comfort of the humans' bed, with only the occasional scaling of the heights by Miss Elizabeth. Once old Bun-Bun arrived, I had to rethink things or risk unconsciousness from inhaling that rancid pilchard breath. And yes – I am reasonably sure it wasn't the EM.

The move to the turtle-shaped footstool was a good one because there is only room for me, so imagine my horror when I trot into the bedroom for my siesta, only to find a fat tortoiseshell creature already ensconced.

I decide to behave in a dignified manner and slap her blotchy little face. Unfortunately, I have underestimated the speed of her reflexes and she sends me spinning across the room with a right hook. I sit down and wash my bottom, mainly because I can't think what else to do.

Days pass and Miss Portia Patch grows weary of my turtle, deciding to join Bun-Bun on the bed. The EM is thrilled at first because she thinks it's lovely for them to be together. This delusion persists until she and Poor Roger are roused by the outbreak of the Great Duvet War at 2am. All that can be seen of Miss Portia are two white paws clinging to the duvet in a doomed attempt to avoid plummeting to the floor, while Bonnie Bun-Bun feigns sleep, rapping her skinny old paw round her face in what she obviously fancies is a beguiling attitude.

'Poor Bun-Bun!' yawns the EM, 'that Portia is a real troublemaker.'

Now, from where I'm sitting (in the depths of the wardrobe), it looks to me as if Portia is the wronged party, but she had it coming so I'm not saying a word.

What's All the Fuss About?

The day starts calmly enough – that is to say, with only the usual level of panic – but soon escalates into Red Alert when Benjamin Wobble stands up just as the EM is tottering out to the pens with a tray full of food for the waifs and strays. Instead of quietly collapsing onto the patio, the EM manages to catapult out from the recesses of the lounge, flinging Kittydins in all directions and crashing down in a kaleidoscope of arms, legs and swear words.

Luckily, Benjamin is unhurt and shows considerable presence of mind by stepping over the EM's fat and writhing body to mop up the food.

For goodness' sake! How much longer is the woman going to lie there! Those poor cats will be desperate for their food. This could become a matter for the RSPCA if she doesn't pull herself together soon.

Another ten minutes pass and she drags herself up, clawing at the wall and making strange moaning noises. Her leg does look a bit strange, but perhaps it's always been like that.

By the time Poor Roger returns from work, the EM has got the hobbling off to a fine art and is beginning to enjoy herself. Benjamin has been forgiven, because nothing is ever his fault, but Elizabeth has made it her business to give him a jab or two with her skinny paw because we were very late with elevenses due to his thoughtlessness.

A few days have passed and the EM is cooking us all a rather sad-looking chicken – a chicken with a "best before" date that shows it to be a contemporary of the woolly mammoth steaks I'm sure I've seen in the darker recesses of the freezer. A glass of El Plonko is at her elbow and she is stirring something that might or might not be gravy in an absentminded way. It's cosy in the kitchen and we're all nodding off. Benjamin has been doing unspeakable things to his stuffed dolphin, but its charms appear to have waned and even he has crashed out across the EM's feet.

44

The last thing anybody needs in this situation is some hysterical woman screaming the place down. Unfortunately, at Tresta Towers, the last thing anybody wants is exactly what we frequently get.

'No! Help! Oh, no!' shrieks the EM, shaking poor Benjamin off her feet and backing across the room with amazing alacrity for one with a "broken" leg. 'Roger! Do something! Where are you?'

Do you know, I'd quite forgotten about that snake I brought in the other day, but there it is, bless it, emerging from under the cooker with its little black tongue flicking away like anything.

There is the most ridiculous fuss, of course. Poor Roger is despatched to find the *Observer's Book of Wild Animals* while the EM stands guard over *my* snake and won't let me have it.

'It's a grass snake!' announces Poor Roger, having read through most of the book and eliminated possibilities such as the Scottish wildcat and red deer.

'Well, we never thought it was a bloody pine marten!' snaps the EM ungratefully. 'That cat's not having it, anyway. Find something to put it in and it can go back to the woods.'

If the neighbours think there's anything strange about a man marching purposefully into the woods with a bread bin under his arm, they have been kind enough to keep their thoughts to themselves. Personally, I find the EM's overreaction to things a continual source of embarrassment. Not to mention the fact that it was *my* snake and she had no right to snatch it away like that. It took me hours to find it, then I had to drag the wretched thing all the way home. If she wants one, she should get down in that drainage ditch and find her own.

A Tick in the Box

I'm just eating my breakfast on the dining room table when the EM runs her podgy hand down my back, then tickles me behind the ears.

'Ugh!' she shouts, parting my fur and recoiling in horror. 'Evie's got a tick! It's repulsive!'

Once again, if further proof were needed, we have evidence of the EM's total inability to cope with the ups and downs of life. The wild cats are always sporting the most impressive ticks. Only the other day, old Skippy had an enormous one on his ear, but somehow this didn't seem to be a major crisis, whereas mine rapidly assumes the proportions of a golf ball in the EM's feverish imagination.

When I mention this to Miss Isabelle, she wrinkles her rather pretty little white nose and says she thinks the dining room table comes into it somehow, a theory supported by the frantic search that ensues when the EM realises the tick is no longer attached to me.

Parasites

The EM and Poor Roger are discussing parasites. How dare they talk about us like that!

I've just realised they are referring to ticks and fleas and something horrible that makes your insides feel all wobbly – w-o-r-m-s. Hours later, the EM returns from the vet's with a carrier bag full of "easy to administer" treatments, which turn out to be about as user-friendly as a microwave oven in a home with no electricity.

Blind Sammy doesn't stand a chance, of course. How the EM can live with herself after sneaking up on that poor defenceless pensioner and emptying the contents of a tube of vile-smelling goo on the back of his neck, I shall never know. At the last minute, Sammy does manage to gnaw her hand but his teeth are so blunt that in her adrenalin-charged state the EM hardly notices.

She doesn't have things all her own way with the Misses Elizabeth and Isabelle, who manage to turn inside their skins so they are teeth and claw sides-up in no time, and she only triumphs with snappy old Cleo because the old bag has her face stuffed into some stolen chicken.

Joan Collins screams the place down when snatched from her boudoir, but Bonnie Bun-Bun is a total let down once she knows there are tuna flakes for lunch. Portia makes her apologies and heads down the garden, while the imaginatively named Katya, who remains a shadowy figure and specialises in making the EM feel guilty by sitting on the doorstep at night, is tricked into submitting behind the dustbins.

While the EM and Poor Roger are discussing, yet again, the advisability of dosing Benjamin Wobble because of his tendency to throw those attention-seeking fits, I decide to nip onto the table for a quick snack. I am reminded of the low cunning that is such a regrettable feature of the EM's character when the wretched woman grabs me by the scruff of the neck and shoves the foul liquid onto my delicate skin.

Eventually they decide to do Benjamin as well, then spend the next three hours worrying that they shouldn't have done and waiting for him to fall on the ground, frothing at the mouth. The reward for all this worrying and waiting is seeing our hero leaping all over that feral tart, Pansy, while the EM and Poor Roger clasp their hands in delight, exclaiming what a little hero Wobble is. We're spoilt for choice when it comes to things to worry about here, but I think the lax standards of the EM and Poor Roger are close to the top of a very long list.

Things that Go Bump in the Night

It is nearly midnight and I'm out here in the garden having a bit of a moth party with my wild friend Spitfire. We've shaken off that silly old Delilah who couldn't catch a moth if it blundered into her mouth, and that tart Pansy who is exhausted after all that frolicking with porky Benjamin. Katya has disappeared into the night and the wild boys – Dennis and Skippy – have been in bed for hours, if the steamy windows in the cat cabins are anything to go by.

In the woods behind the garden there are all sorts of noises associated with those pointy-faced badgers and smelly old foxes, but suddenly a far more disturbing noise pierces the darkness.

Spitfire mutters, 'Don't look now, but there's a whale in a nightdress by the patio door!'

'Well, send me to the vet's if it isn't the old EM!' I snigger. For it is no other than the EM, calling me in.

'Come on, Evie!' she trills, 'you don't want to be out there all night. *Anything* could happen!'

Yeah. Like I might enjoy myself! I'm not going in, not while there are all these yummy moths to catch.

After a bit, the EM tries the old lights out technique which has been known to work with less intelligent cats such as Miss Isabelle, who tends to fling herself into the kitchen if she thinks she really is going to be left out all night.

Eventually, the EM calls it a night and totters off to bed. Now that all the lights are out, the moths have cleared off as well so a lot of the fun has gone out of things. Still, one has one's pride and I'm determined to stay out for a while to make the point.

A couple of hours have passed and I'm beginning to feel a bit chilly. Spitfire has disappeared to do whatever feral cats do at night, and the rest of the wild bunch are asleep, looking more like badly stuffed toys than finely honed killers. The top bedroom window is open a fraction and I think I should be able to scrabble through.

Made it! I plummet down the other side, only to catch my toe on that stupid silk flower thing she's got on the windowsill. Mercifully, I haven't hurt myself, which is more than can be said for the poor bloody plant pot.

The EM sits bolt upright as I land on what feels like a hot water bottle but must be her stomach. 'I'll swing for that cat!' she screams, flailing about but missing me by inches. I leap for the pillow, but unfortunately catch her nose which starts to bleed. Luckily, none of it goes on my fur but the fuss she makes is unbelievable. Poor Roger almost wakes up, but thinks better of it even in his sleep, having experienced a host of damaging nocturnal crises since he moved in.

I settle down at last, draping myself round the EM's head, only to wake up when a volcano-like rumble erupts a few inches away. It is Miss Elizabeth, who has perfected the art of the open-mouthed purr. This is absolutely terrifying, rising above the EM's snuffling and Poor Roger's snoring in a rasping rattle.

I poke her flabby white undercarriage but this only increases the volume. In the end I decide that I am, after all, a feral cat and return to the relative tranquillity of the garden, where the only things to contend with are the entire cast of *Jurassic Park* with a few vampires thrown in.

CHAPTER SEVEN

Alarms and Excursions

It is late and the EM has lurched off to have her bath. Poor Roger is snoring away on the sofa underneath Benjamin and Miss Isabelle, and Sammy is dribbling into his sleeping bag. I am stretched across the top of the cat activity centre – a misnomer if ever there was as we only use it for sleeping on.

A sudden scream and a noise like a tidal wave disturb the peace. The EM has slipped over in the bath and there's more water over the floor than you would find in the average Olympic swimming pool.

In the morning, Poor Roger is surprised to find her in an emotional state as she struggles to empty the dishwasher. He paws at her in a sympathetic manner, only to be screamed at because she thinks she's fractured a rib. After dealing manfully with 151 dirt trays and taking Master Benjamin to see his consultant, Poor Roger suddenly begins to see the advantages of being at work and heads off to Guildford with a bracing wave.

The EM perks up as the day progresses, and by the time she's had a few visitors and more sympathy than is good for her, she has perfected the *Hunchback of Notre Dame* walk.

As the days go by, the old girl rallies, and by the time that Poor Roger is coping with a dual diagnosis of nervous exhaustion and hypothermia, she feels strong enough to bin the painkillers and rely on the generally more enjoyable qualities of a full-bodied El Plonko.

The Gathering

The pressure is on. Usually, Poor Roger is pathetically pleased to see supper appear before 10 o'clock but this evening the EM has already provided a nutritious microwaved meal and flung the dishes into the dishwasher and it's only 6.30. Poor Roger has been "encouraged" to pursue his interests in the "study", which means he has been banished to the cupboard which doubles as the computer room and Joan Collins' boudoir.

Meanwhile, the EM is "tidying up" – a rarely performed household duty in this establishment which consists of shoving magazines and chocolate wrappers into the boot of the car and kicking quantities of cat litter under various mats. Usually I'd be outside hanging around till Spitfire returns from the woods, but as the EM so obviously wants me to go out, I've resolved to sit on the sofa and wash Sammy's head for him.

It soon becomes horribly clear that the EM is having some sort of gathering as various odd people arrive, enquiring after the EM's health. Once they've got that out of the way, they get on to the important stuff, including whether Sammy is managing better with the new style puppy pads and is Bun-Bun's "looseness" less apparent since she was weaned off Poor Roger's breakfast leftovers.

As people arrive, the EM ushers them in and suggests

to me that I might like to pop outside as it's such "a lovely evening". Well I wouldn't and it isn't, so I settle down on top of Sammy, who seems to be rather excited by this sudden intimacy.

As yet another person crams onto the sofa, I begin to feel a bit feral and do a bit of low level growling, then decide it's all too much and leap up, causing a mass spillage of tea, coffee and biscuits. By now the Cats Protection Committee – because that's what this is all about – are having to put their money where their mouths are as they mop themselves down and salvage their agendas. It wouldn't look too good for them to start shrieking at poor little Evie, would it?

Having made my escape, I run round to the patio door and concentrate on looking storm-tossed. Every time someone gets up to let me in, I rush off into the darkness, then come back as soon as they've settled down.

Blind Sammy, who usually spends the entire evening asleep on his cushion, is causing considerable disruption by tottering about in a random and senile manner, barging into people's legs and handbags and howling dementedly because he can't find the door to the kitchen. This is getting to the EM, who keeps yelling at people to move things out of Sammy's way, and it isn't doing much for anybody else as they're still on item 1 of the agenda an hour later.

Predictably, Miss Elizabeth is the only one having a lovely time. When Lizzie's mother rejected her at 4 weeks of age (one of her better decisions), the EM had to hand-rear the wretched thing and get her back legs working as she couldn't move them. All this attention has made

Miss Elizabeth what she is today: a pain in the bottom. The EM continues to be entranced by Lizzie's behaviour, while the rest of us could cheerfully shove her down the badger sett. Peering inside now I can see her, raking at people's arms and leering into their faces – it's enough to make them rip up their membership cards and rush off to join the Dogs' Trust.

Abandoned

It's happened again! The usual round of slobbery kisses and endless cuddles, then they're rattling off on holiday in the old tin box without a backward glance. We don't care that much, actually, because we've got Auntie K looking after us and she's no trouble.

It's evening and Auntie K has slumped back on the sofa, having lost the will to live after reading the EM's "Helpful Notes". She was coping quite well till she got to the bit about Bun-Bun's lunches, which occur every hour on the hour and *must* be well mashed.

This is closely followed by the guidance about Sammy's puppy pads as he now favours the ones with the blue plastic backing. The positioning of the said pads is crucial – and lethal to the unsuspecting, located as they are on a shiny wooden floor. A certain amount of overlapping is also required, seepage being a constant threat.

Auntie K has all but nodded off when a strange and insistent noise intrudes. There is a text message on her mobile phone.

"Hope all's well. Wet and windy here." It's the EM, of course, worrying about us from the wilds of Scotland.

Goodness knows what they've had for supper. She's obviously got indigestion.

Auntie K dutifully jabs at the phone. "All good here. Benjamin and Sammy on sofa. Enjoy your break!"

We settle down, only to have the peace shattered once again by the insistent "peep" of the mobile. What a surprise! It's the EM again.

"Glad the boys are fine. What about everybody else?" Auntie K, who is a kindly soul, pulls a few faces and messages back: "Everybody very happy. Don't worry about anything."

Silence follows. I can imagine the scene in their Highland retreat: Poor Roger tottering in from the depths of the woodshed where he has been gathering fuel and gashing every digit in the process, to be greeted with the EM's lengthy speech on loyalty. "K says the cats are all very happy. What she means is, they're not missing us at all. After all I've done for them!" Next will come the bit about Greyfriars Bobby obviously not being a cat, and after another glass or two of El Plonko it'll be the stuff about changing her will.

Lead Kindly Light

They're back from Scotland. It is a cold dark night and the EM is out in the cat pens providing room service to the waifs and strays. She is in with Monica – a strange little creature with more problems than you could throw an agony aunt at. Monica is behaving quite well this evening until she looks over the EM's shoulder and utters an unearthly scream.

The EM turns round and follows suit. Unfortunately,

she is too large to follow Monica into the safety of her heated cat house, but gives every indication that she'd be quite keen on the idea.

The cause of this consternation is a flashing light, some feet above the ground, which is making its way out of the shadows at the bottom of the garden and looming towards Monica's pen at an alarming rate.

'Whatever's that? For God's sake! Who is it?' splutters the EM as the light finally draws alongside the Perspex window.

'It's only me!' replies Poor Roger. 'I've been down to open the badger tunnel! This miner's lamp's really good.'

'Didn't you realise you were flashing?' snaps the EM. 'You've frightened Monica sick – and you look ridiculous with that thing on your head.'

The Great Escape, Starring Bonnie Bun-Bun

I don't know quite how it's happened, but the volunteers who come here to help out with the waifs and strays have become quite a fixture. The amazing thing is that they seem to be frighteningly normal but have nonetheless become the EM's cronies – presumably on the "if you can't beat them, join them" principle.

This is the situation this evening. A glamorous young woman is draped against the back door, engaged in a rather raucous conversation about cats and men and the relative usefulness of each species. The EM is cackling away while poking half-heartedly at something which might be the badgers' supper or possibly something extra special for Poor Roger's tea.

Suddenly the young woman flings open the back

door. 'It's ok for Cleo to go out, isn't it?' she asks as a skinny tabby legs it into the night.

The EM glances at Cleo, who is asleep on the worktop. 'It's fine,' she hisses, 'but that wasn't Cleo! Who the bloody hell did you let out?'

They rush outside in time to see the ancient Bonnie Bun-Bun leaping across the green opposite like a particularly animated gazelle. Poor Roger is dragged away from the computer screen to help form a pincer movement while 18-year-old Bun-Bun skips and dances amongst the trees and succeeds in making three adult humans look extremely stupid.

Just as the EM is on the brink of a hysterical outburst, an unlikely hero appears in the shape of Mungo, a huge and challenged shaggy dog, who is returning from his evening stroll. Bun-Bun is momentarily transfixed by the sight of the dog and hesitates just long enough for Poor Roger and our glamorous friend to grab her.

It's slightly unfortunate that one grabs one end and one the other, so that for a moment poor Bun-Bun looks destined to assume the proportions of a tabby Dachshund.

CHAPTER EIGHT

Winter Wonderland

It's November and colder than particularly cold cat sick. This is a testing time for the old ferals – or would be if they weren't snuggled down in their cabins with more duvets than your average luxury hotel. With the first snow, in comes our ancient feral boy, Skippy, who sweeps past the EM as she opens the patio door and heads purposefully for the spare bedroom to select his winter quarters. He commandeers a large and bouncy pile of bedclothes and growls menacingly the moment anybody appears in the doorway. I am consumed with a grudging admiration for the ghastly old thing and think I might offer to marry him.

Deja Mew

Earlier this year we had a lot of weeping and wailing when the old mop head, also known as Miss Calico, sicked up her last fur ball and went to the great dirt tray in the sky. Miss Calico was an almost pedigree Persian, with all the design faults of that unfortunate breed. She didn't actually believe in dirt trays and was noted for piddling copiously on the bathroom floor – not to mention leaving a treasure trail of other surprises which would have given the Health and Safety Executive a field day, had they chosen to visit. Wisely, perhaps, they decided to give Tresta Towers a miss.

Anyway, I digress. The EM and Poor Roger were besotted with this apology for a cat and a great sadness descended on the sofa when our little fuzzy friend departed. Months have passed and even Poor Roger can almost talk about Calico without crying.

It is Sunday morning and the phone ringing is an unwelcome intrusion into my dream; this time, a vet is being eaten by a pointy-faced ferret. I was sitting next to one recently and was rather fascinated by his twitchy little face – the ferret I mean, although come to think of it...

The EM launches herself at the phone. 'Oh, thank God for that!' cries the EM in response to some unidentifiable gibbering. 'Yes, of course! Bring her in – we're all ready.'

I'm just subsiding back into my dream and the ferret is licking his blood-covered chops in the cutest way, when a car swoops into the drive and a young woman leaps out, clutching a cat carrier.

'Can you believe it?' she storms, 'the poor little thing hasn't even got a name!'

Quite honestly, looking at this bundle of fur at the back of the cat carrier, I would have thought that being nameless was the least of the creature's problems. The EM pops the carrier into the pen and leaves the bundle to emerge in its own time.

A bit later, having visited the newcomer, the EM staggers back into the kitchen and adopts a theatrical pose. 'You are not going to believe this,' she declares, 'but that cat is the same colour as dear Calico!'

My heart sinks as I am gripped by a terrible premonition. I sidle out to give the thing the once-over. It is a Persian – a proper one with a walked-into-a-wall face, streaming eyes and candyfloss instead of fur. And yes – the candyfloss is grey, orange and white. Just like Miss Calico.

And we thought Calico had problems! The new arrival has got a runny bottom – never good news at the best of times, but disastrous in someone with such fluffy pantaloons – bad teeth, knotted fur and a lump on its face. They've called it "Bella", but as I've said before, the EM has a vivid imagination. She keeps saying to this poor old fluffball, 'We've called you that because you will be beautiful! Everybody will love Bella and be desperate to give her a home!'

I was right. The wretched thing will be here forever.

A few days later I come bouncing into the lounge to find a huge cage has been erected and remember it's the cage that I was banged up in when I first arrived here. Sure enough, there's my igloo – and, surprise, surprise, there's the old fluffball inside!

She's not just "Bella" now, of course. She's "Bella Calico Munchkin-Cook" and we're stuck with her.

I manage to wake Miss Isabelle up and ask her why she isn't making a fuss about a perfectly strange (and I mean strange) cat being brought indoors. 'This is *our* home,' I hiss into her velvety little black ear, 'we don't want some old pedigree tart moving in!'

Now, I've always realised that Isabelle is not particularly gifted, but I am a bit taken aback by the response. Apparently, Bella is not a new cat, according to my piebald friend. She is in fact Miss Calico, who happened to be out in the garden for rather a long time.

When in Doubt, Have a Crisis

It's been all go this morning. We had the usual gang of volunteers round first thing – bless their hearts; even after years of turning up every Saturday, they still come to lavish kisses and cuddles on the waifs and strays in the pens. Poor Roger looks forward to these visits because for once he gets a bit of attention and chocolate biscuits, and if he took up residence in a cat pen he would probably get the kisses and cuddles as well.

While all this is going on, the EM is busy preparing delicious goodies for her long-suffering mother, who they will be visiting shortly. Never one to choose the simple option if a complicated solution is on the cards, the EM has decided to home a miserable looking tabby on the way. Except, of course, it's not on the way, as Poor Roger and numerous maps have pointed out.

They are ready to leave when the EM suddenly feels inspired to check that all the vulnerable cats are safely incarcerated, in case they get eaten by badgers or lost in the woods. None of this concern applies to me, of course, because I am a proper cat; heaven help the badger that laid his grubby, worm-raking paws on me!

Anyway, they're both rushing about like lunatics when they realise that Bella is missing. A frantic rooting through cupboards and wardrobes fails to locate old Fluffy Knickers, so they fling themselves round the garden, grovelling under bushes and – for some reason best known to themselves – staring up into the trees on the edge of the wood. Considering the Persian struggles to get on to the dining room table, it hardly seems likely that she's ensconced at the top of a 100-foot beech tree.

The patio door flies open and the EM leaps into the room, snatches up a torch and falls to the floor in a dramatic manner. The fitful beam is directed behind the sofa where, alongside a pile of mummified dinosaur remains, a candyfloss bottom is reversing towards the light. The stupid Persian appears to have fallen down the gap at the other end and has been unable to get out.

The reunion is a touching one, or would be if it wasn't so sickening. Poor old Bella is all shaky, the EM and Poor Roger are in the most terrible state, and I'm just off out to shake up those podgy pigeons!

An Accident Waiting to Happen

The first sunny day for ages has gone to the EM's head and she has decided to scrub out the dirt trays. We have seven indoors, each the size of a small swimming pool, so this is more of an undertaking than it might sound. Things are progressing well, with only minimal spillage, when a crony of hers turns up at the back door.

In the seconds it takes the EM to let her in, Benjamin Wobble has decided he simply must have a little tiddle and has climbed into an empty tray to perform. This inevitably means his cute little ginger feet are soaked, but as if this isn't enough of a drama, he then wobbles over and emerges to drip all over the place.

The EM blames herself, luckily for Benjamin, and the next hour is spent apologising to the ginger lump and sending out for more baby wipes. The friend clearly regrets her decision to pop in for a cuppa when Benjamin rubs round her ankles and flops over her shoes. It is immediately evident that the cheaper baby wipes favoured by the EM do not have the absorbent properties of their more expensive counterparts.

Later, another misguided and vulnerable woman turns up with some cat beds and blankets. She glimpses what she takes to be a heap of feather dusters on the floor and nearly suffers a heart attack when the heap struggles to its fuzzy little feet.

'Whatever's that?' she squeaks, retreating towards the back door.

The EM laughs a tinkling – and extremely irritating – laugh. 'Oh, that's Princess Bella,' she chirrups, 'she escaped from Russia with Anastasia. They stowed away in laundry baskets. Anastasia's working in Tesco's in Addlestone and Bella has come to live with us.'

I glare across at the EM – a look intended to convey exasperation and contempt, but it's water off a particularly insensitive duck's back.

Our visitor is by now showing signs of naked and totally understandable terror and I am clawing at the locked cat flap. Being chased by that marauding tom would be fun compared to this.

The "No" Word

The EM's failings are far too numerous to list, but one of the most conspicuous is her total inability to take "no" for an answer.

This morning, I experience a deep sense of unease on entering the kitchen, where the EM is lovingly preparing Poor Roger's lunchbox, closely watched by Miss

Elizabeth, who is helping with the sandwich making. As I crunch my way through my yummy cat biscuits, the EM turns and smiles at me.

'There's my little Evie!' she trills, 'pretty as a picture. Let me get you some more biscuits, sweetie. Those look a bit dry.'

Most people would obviously realise that it is in the nature of biscuits to be slightly on the dry side, but the EM is often some way behind the rest of the population. As she bends down to replenish the bowl, she starts stroking my neck and then grasps the scruff in an experimental sort of way. At this point, my uneasiness gives way to fully-fledged panic and I bolt into the wardrobe.

Not for the first time, the EM astonishes me with a display of such low cunning that I find myself almost admiring her. The admiration wears off pretty quickly when I emerge after a couple of hours to be scruffed by the wretched woman, who is clutching an evil-looking syringe in her right hand and looking horribly determined in a mottled kind of way.

I do the only thing I can and twist round as far as possible with a view to severing one of her more important arteries, but she has me in a grip of steel. When I think how she goes on about her arthritis! Well, if her treatment of me is anything to go by, the woman could be an Olympic athlete.

She shoves the needle in, but I manage to pull away and most of the evil goo runs over the kitchen floor. I then run screaming into the wardrobe and Poor Roger accuses the EM of frightening me. Frightening me! That doesn't even come close. How would anybody feel with some lumpy old human strangling them and shoving needles in them?

Anyway, I am so cheered by their spirited exchange of views that I decide to emerge from the wardrobe and sit on the EM's computer for the rest of the day. This drives her wild, but she's stuck with it or there could well be a referral to the RSPCA.

Things Are Going Too Well

I can't remember the last time I enjoyed myself so much! The EM is on the phone to some beleaguered person who adopted one of her wretched waifs less than 24 hours ago.

'And what part of the advice about keeping him in for three weeks did you find particularly hard to understand?' snaps the EM, jabbing at her notepad and spilling coffee over Miss Elizabeth's bed.

There is a brief interlude while the person on the other end of the phone gibbers and sobs.

'So your boyfriend thought it would be a good idea to open the bathroom window? And was he surprised when the cat disappeared through it? And what exactly are you planning to do about it?'

More muffled sobbing and squeaking emanates from the receiver.

'Get out there and search for him!' screams the EM, 'and when you've searched, go out and search some more! That poor defenceless cat is probably terrified. He's lost in a strange place and anything could happen to him. And all thanks to your dodo of a boyfriend!'

The receiver crashes down, the remainder of the coffee

splashes over Lizzie's bed, and the EM snatches up the mop to give the kitchen floor a good seeing to.

It's nearly suppertime and the EM has spent a miserable day imagining what could have happened to the lost waif. This means that we've all had a miserable day, including Poor Roger, who is beginning to wonder how long it will be before the whole sorry episode will be deemed to be his fault.

The phone rings. It is the owner of the missing waif. The EM prepares to deliver a few more home truths before she realises that they've actually found the cat and got him safely indoors. Relief reduces her to simpering gratitude, which isn't nearly as entertaining as incoherent rage.

Two days pass uneventfully, when another phone call sees a resurgence of the incoherent rage. This time the waif is trashing the place, refusing to use a litter tray and growling at everybody in a menacing way.

'I don't believe it!' shrieks the EM. 'He was just the sweetest creature in the cat pen, and so clean! He must be upset about something.'

More babbling, then the EM looks as if she's about to explode. 'Bring him back? You've only had him a couple of days! He needs to settle down and feel safe – not be bundled back here. You haven't given him a chance!'

Anyway, it seems the writing is on the wall and the next morning a rather unrepentant-looking black and white cat is returned to be cooed over and welcomed back into the fold. His erstwhile owner beats a hasty retreat, which is probably the most sensible thing she's done for a long time.

'Mark my words,' says Miss Elizabeth in a rather

puffed up way, 'that cat will end up staying here. Did you see the creepy way he sucked up to the EM? I've seen it all before and no doubt I'll see it again.'

'But she said she could never have a boy cat called "Jess",' squeaks Miss Isabelle. 'She always said she couldn't stand Postman Pat.'

Miss Elizabeth and I look at each other knowingly. It's touching to think that Isabelle has lived here for thirteen years and still hasn't got a clue.

What's In a Name?

A few days have limped by and the EM has been talking a lot about a cat called "Geoffrey" who is apparently coming to join our little family.

Isabelle is thrilled. 'That means she's forgotten all about that awful Jess,' she lisps innocently.

An Extra Plate

Well, that's it. The wretched thing is in the kitchen, up on the work top, tucking into a plate of yummy cat food and looking up at the EM as if she's a fat and rather unsophisticated goddess.

'I hope you like that, Geoffrey,' she whispers, and is ridiculously thrilled when the great lump twitches an ear and delivers an ear-shattering burp.

The Persian – never the sharpest pooper-scooper in the box – comments that she hasn't ever seen Isabelle on the work top before.

'You haven't now, Fuzzy Chops,' I hiss, 'that's the new boy. That's old Geoffrey. He's about twice the size of

Isabelle and his white bits aren't in the same places. And he's a boy, if that means anything to you.'

At that moment, Geoffrey looks straight at me and plummets off the work top. He growls at me and chases me into the bedroom with the EM in hot pursuit.

By this time, I'm screaming my head off and the EM grabs Geoffrey by the scruff of the neck and marches him into the garden. I dive into the wardrobe and hide amongst the EM's shoes – not always a happy experience, but preferable to being mugged by that piebald hooligan.

Result!

My nerves are in shreds. Every time I poke my little head round the corner of the garage, Geoffrey flies after me and chases me into the woods. I've had to stay out for two whole days, the only consolation being that the EM and Poor Roger have spent hours calling me and shaking the biscuits in a doomed attempt to lure me in, so I have not suffered alone.

Eventually, I manage to give Geoffrey the slip and scramble in through the bedroom window. The EM and Poor Roger make a great fuss of me, which is gratifying.

'I know she's being really irritating,' announces the EM, 'but I think Geoffrey will have to go and live somewhere else. We can't have little Evie's life made a misery.'

Leaving aside the "irritating" bit, I like the sound of this. In due course, a plan is put together and it is agreed that Geoffrey will go and live with a friend of theirs called Ruth.

Ruth tries to put off having Geoffrey by having open-heart surgery at the last moment, but there is an inevitability about it all and off he goes within minutes of her regaining consciousness.

CHAPTER NINE

A Party of Persians

I never thought the EM would re-home old Geoffrey. In fact, as I remarked to Miss Isabelle, I thought it was considerably more likely that I'd marry a toothy old guinea pig. Well, bring on my diminutive and buck-toothed groom because not only has Geoffrey gone, but apparently he doesn't want to come back.

The EM has just returned from a visit to see how Geoffrey and Ruth are getting along and apparently they're so besotted with each other they couldn't wait for the EM to clear off. The EM is pretending she's not upset, but she is. I can always tell because they sit there on the sofa, holding hands. That's the EM and Blind Sammy, of course – not the EM and Poor Roger.

Versions of Persians

Miss Elizabeth has just rushed in with disturbing news. She is squeaking so frantically that for a moment I think my guinea pig has arrived. She has been listening to yet another alarming phone conversation – we rarely have any other sort here – and thinks that trouble could be looming.

Apparently the EM was talking to a veterinary nurse who was trying to find somewhere for an old wreck of a

Persian to end its days. The EM made some feeble remark about already having one of those, as if that would let her off the hook, but Nursey had other ideas.

A few days passed and nothing more was heard, possibly because we had other excitements, including Poor Roger retiring from paid work – I stress the "paid" bit because we all know his feet won't touch the ground now. Still, it's not like the EM to let a few parties and presentations get in the way of a project.

It's four days later that the blow falls. The EM clears her throat in an exaggerated manner. 'So I thought Boris could go in a kitten pen where the telly used to be. He can see out into the garden from there and he'll have plenty of company.'

Poor Roger looks at us and we look at him. Did we miss something? Has there been a long and reasoned discussion about Boris joining the home team? Why can none of us remember it? Because, of course, there hasn't been. This is just the EM's way of dealing with things and we should all be used to it by now.

The next morning a car pulls up and two fresh-faced veterinary nurses leap out clutching what appears to be a rolled-up towel with some wool sticking out both ends. This, it turns out, is Boris – a pedigree smoke Persian. Well, you could have fooled me!

Boris is about 100 years old and has been shaved. He sports a trendy crew cut on his head, has fetching little woolly boots and a lion-like tuft at the end of a tail which resembles frayed rope. He also has cauliflower ears. He was found wandering the streets and the RSPCA couldn't trace an owner. Well, honestly, did they really think someone would admit to owning that?

There is great excitement because Princess Bella's fur is growing after a protracted flirtation with every allergy known to man and cat, and she looks a little less like a particularly bald beetroot. She loves going out in the garden and we all have to pretend to chase the silly creature so that she can chase us back, with her stumpy little legs all stiff and her back arched.

And we're learning more about Boris every day. In fact, it took hardly any time at all to find out that he hasn't got a clue about dirt trays and even less about puppy pads, so we're rapidly emptying the shelves of kitchen rolls and anything that looks as if it could have absorbent properties – like stale sponge cakes, for example.

Boris likes to live dangerously and has no sooner been released from the confines of the kitten pen than he decides to take up residence by the front door, only to risk life and limb every time the postman calls. I believe the patent is pending for the ingenious and possibly life-saving contraption the EM and Poor Roger have rigged up, but to me it looks suspiciously like a sheet of cardboard wedged under the letterbox. This sophisticated invention has caused a few problems, such as the phone almost being cut off due to non-payment of bills, as the cardboard sheet tends to deflect mail (particularly important mail) down the side of the scratching post where there is a strong possibility that it will never be seen again.

I have grown dangerously fond of Boris because he has a most attractive and wayward sense of humour. The kitten pen, which is such a talking point in the lounge, is used to bang him up when the EM and Poor Roger judge that a steaming pudding or a puddle could be imminent. Well, that old Persian can certainly hang on! As soon as the door of the pen is open, he clambers out on those terrible knobbly little legs and heads off for an inaccessible corner, where he digs loudly and relentlessly. This results in Poor Roger catapulting off the sofa, crawling under the sideboard, and dragging the old scarecrow out before he's performed.

One Day My Prints Will Come

In the rare moments between dirt tray duties and bedtime, Poor Roger has been indulging in some rather fancy photography. He's joined the local Photographic Society (which the EM insists on calling a "Club") and is actually taking some pretty mean photographs. There is a particularly irresistible one of me looking quite lovely in a moody kind of way and I've made sure that the EM has it on her desk to inspire her – if indeed anything could raise her sights above the price of El Plonko and puppy pads.

On their recent travels – well, a trip to Cork and back – the EM was missing us so much that at dinner on the first evening she extracted a bundle of photos from her battered handbag and forced the bemused couple on the next table to look at them. When she handed them the one of Boris, they held it upside down for a while before realising the error of their ways, the absence of ears making it particularly tricky to orientate oneself.

A few days later, we heard that some poor soul had

jumped off the very cruise ship they had been on. I mean, I know Boris' photo was pretty scary, but it seems just a tad extreme.

Where There's a Will, There's a Panic

This is when it happens, of course. Everything is ticking along nicely and the phone rings.

The EM is doing her patient but exasperated voice. 'Yes, I know you've phoned about flea treatments and I realise I probably won't know them, but could you please just tell me who's died?'

Seconds later we are left in no doubt that the EM did indeed know the unfortunate couple. It also seems that she has inherited their cat.

The appointed day dawns and the EM goes clattering off in the long-suffering tin box to collect little Lucio. She returns lugging a black bruiser the size of a spaniel who Benjamin Wobble immediately falls in love with. The fact that Lucio hates the sight of this flabby ginger pudding only makes him more desirable in the deluded one's eyes.

Lucio and his various suitcases are promptly installed in the spare bedroom and we are just as promptly banished to the other side of the door.

Getting Rid of the Old Skip

As if we don't have enough excitement with the arrival of the new boy, Miss Isabelle has just overheard a snatch of conversation which has raised a few feline eyebrows.

'Yes,' trilled the EM, 'let's get rid of the old skip today. We've finished with it, haven't we?'

Rewind to the care that was lavished on poor old Skippy the feral when he moved in for the winter and reflect on the fickleness of human nature! I know the creature is obviously well past his sell-by date, but he's not alone there. Is this the start of a hideous plan to replace all the old wrecks with new models?

Hours later we huddle in the hallway as a huge lorry thing backs down the drive, smashing playfully into the guttering before grunting to a halt. Miss Elizabeth is the first to have the Eureka moment – the skip is not in fact the scraggy old feline dribbling under the beech tree, but the metal monstrosity in the front garden.

The Ancient Hippy

For some time now, the EM has been sporting a rather exaggerated limp – usually but not exclusively on the right side. This has been an annoyance for several of us, as it causes her to head off randomly, barging into coffee tables and dirt trays and generally causing havoc. Blind Sammy remarked, "Is she having a laugh or what?" when they collided disastrously en route to the patio door this morning.

I wouldn't mind so much if I didn't suspect that she was doing it on purpose because of my own little crisis. Oh, I don't want to bore anyone with my life-threatening condition because I'm sure there are a lot of cats with more serious things, but if you insist... It's a lump actually. No – I'm not talking about Benjamin Wobble, who gets porkier by the day; I am in fact referring to a suspect lump under my chin which the EM discovered last week.

Poor Roger is very worried about me and even the EM is burdened with guilt because she thinks the stress of the Geoffrey episode might have been too much for a highly-strung little feline such as me. The vet has been called and I'm shut in the front room. If they think I'm going to let some strange woman wipe her fumbling fingers over me...

I've been in the bottom of the wardrobe for hours amongst the EM's ghastly old shoes. The vet has rushed off, licking her wounds, and my so-called friends are tucking into their lunch without so much as a twitch of the whisker for their sick colleague. The EM has booked me in for "investigative surgery" next week.

Like It or Lump It

Tomorrow is the day and if it hadn't been blinding down with rain I would have left home by now.

Here comes the EM now – cooing and making ridiculous kissy noises. I just know that she's going to start making a fuss of me and telling me what a beautiful girl I am. For one thing, she's only doing it because she feels sorry for me, and secondly, why doesn't she try telling me something I don't know?

Minutes later, I'm one very happy pussycat and it's not just because the EM has left the room. The lump has gone! She poked and prodded with her sausage-like fingers and couldn't find it! The theory is that my gland must have popped up when that tick the size of a grape latched on to me. Well, I never thought I'd feel warmly towards a tick, but I could almost find it in my furry little heart to embrace the bloated lump.

Bun-Bun is the first to burst through the barricades that separate the new boy from the rest of us. As the EM goes in with his breakfast, the old tabby scarecrow nips in behind her. We wait anxiously for explosive sound effects but all is tranquil. When the door opens, the EM emerges with an unrepentant Bun-Bun tucked firmly under her arm.

'Well?' squeaks Miss Elizabeth, 'was he very frightening?'

Bun-Bun is washing her face in an exaggerated and intensely irritating manner but pauses briefly to declare that breakfast was absolutely yummy.

'But what about the cat?' we chorus, barely able to suppress an urge to snap Bun-Bun's scraggy neck.

'Cat?' murmurs Bun-Bun absently. 'I don't remember much about him. But the breakfast was delicious.'

A few hours have passed and the EM has decided to let Lucio out of his room to have a look round. I think for a moment that the sun has gone behind a cloud, but it's this great lumpy cat blocking out the light as he stands in the doorway, rooted to the spot. He looks round the room in wonderment, taking in Blind Sammy's snoring form, Boris' Mohican and Benjamin Wobble, who is enthusiastically bonking his bed. I suppose it's hardly surprising that when he sees me elegantly perched on the top of the scratching tower, Lucio falls hopelessly and deeply in love. I almost manage to suppress a yawn and then spit straight between his rather gorgeous eyes.

The EM's morning treat – once she's emptied the trays, dished out copious amounts of cat food and administered medication by the ton – is to sit down and giggle inanely at her emails. She is usually followed into the "study" by a cup of coffee so strong that it makes its own way in, and by me because most of the emails are for me anyway. By the time we are sitting comfortably – well, I am; she's usually perched on the edge of the chair with my dear little paws pummelling her kidneys – it's not far off lunchtime for the people who inhabit Planet Normal. Luckily, we are not troubled by such conventions here, lunch being a very movable feast if it ever appears at all.

This morning there is a particularly sad communication from one of her cronies, lamenting the fact that the one thing she ever wants to watch on the telly is Wimbledon and her cat won't let her. The cat in question is an impish white creature called Charlie and, needless to say, Charlie was homed with this unfortunate woman by none other than the EM herself. At first, I wonder whatever Charlie could be doing. Is this diminutive tyrant attacking her every time she advances nervously towards the TV set? Has he commandeered the remote control? Is he insisting on watching *The Aristocats* for the umpteenth time whenever Wimbledon is on?

The truth is that Charlie actually shares his mother's passion and feels the need to launch himself at the TV every time the ball flies across the screen. When it disappears from view, Charlie ricochets round the room, eventually concluding that the ball must be inside the set somewhere. So convinced is he that he leaps astride the TV, where he hangs, obscuring most of the screen until the next swipe of the ball sends him into orbit again.

The EM chortles merrily for about ten minutes, then bashes out a rather insensitive reply, suggesting that her friend tries aversion therapy to discourage Charlie's unhelpful behaviour. This would entail dressing up as a tennis ball and leaping out on the poor cat. Exactly.

There are always several emails featuring either whimsical photographs of cute cats and kittens curled upon the backs of dinosaurs or rib-ticklingly amusing ones entitled, "How to Give a Cat a Pill", or "How to Bath a Pussycat". This morning, however, there is a really good video about cats growing opposing thumbs and taking over the world. I love it, but the EM seems to find it quite scary.

I Dream a Dream – My Evita Moment

Or, to put it another way, today the Special Needs Unit – tomorrow, the world.

I realise now what's been holding me back – apart from the EM and Poor Roger, I mean. Now that dear Lucio and I have become what is colloquially known as "an item", I see that behind every strong and glamorous girl cat there is a handsome and fairly malleable boy.

I spend many happy hours planning exactly when and how I shall break it to the EM and Poor Roger that they are yesterday's news and that I shall be running things from now on. It was the EM's hip that made me realise that the poor old thing is past it and that it would be a kindness to take over. As for Poor Roger – he can carry on with his photography and even pop along to Club Night as long as he doesn't get uppity.

I shall be a kindly and inspiring leader with my dearest Lucio by my side – or possibly standing a few paces behind me – but I shan't put up with any lippiness from the EM, or for that matter from that old fur-covered coat-hanger, Miss Bonnie Bun-Bun.

Blind Sammy might be a bit of a problem, as he's pretty besotted with the EM, but they can carry on dribbling and snoring on the sofa, so no change there.

In fact, that's the only thing against it. On bad days I think I could take over here and it wouldn't really make much difference, because everything would chug on just the same. I could be making some really dramatic and stirring speech and old Boris would do a steaming pudding, Benjamin would wobble over to look and fall in it, and Bella would sit scratching herself into a coma.

Yes, I know. There isn't any real reason why a lovely and gifted black cat couldn't rule the world, but if the rest of the world is anything like this place, she might decide that it's really not worth the effort.